THE TOTALLY AWESOME PHISH TRIVIA BOOK

Uncover The History With Facts Every
Phish Head Should Know!

ISBN: 978-1-955149-03-7

By

Dale Raynes

Please consider writing a review on our Amazon book page. Thank you and we hope you enjoy this book!

TABLE OF CONTENTS

INTRODUCTION

Phish is an American rock band known for its use of eclectic, unconventional instruments and extended improvisation. Founded in 1983, Phish's music is notorious for its unusual influences. The Phish sound was inspired by various styles, including jazz fusion, funk, bluegrass, and psychedelic rock. The 1980s era of rock consisted mainly of heavy metal and synth-pop elements. In a sea of bands trying to crawl to the top of fame and success, Phish emerged triumphantly with a unique sound. The band emphasized live performances and improvisation, often incorporating the audience into their songs and sets on the spot. The band made sure that no two shows were ever the same. Few musical groups share Phish's dedication to diversity and originality.

Phish's celebrated music largely rose to popularity during the late '80s and early '90s. The band is still active today, meaning they have been playing their unmatchable style for upwards of 30 years. Their projected aesthetic of going against the grain and striving to be different from everyone else has appealed to Americans far and wide for decades. The band has been named as a source of inspiration and influence for several other musical groups, including Umphrey's McGee and Disco Biscuits. To remind us of the beginning, the middle, the state of the band today, and every tidbit of information in between, *Phish - History & Trivia* is here to refresh and uphold the legacy of the long-lived and loved rock band.

This trivia book covers the origins and influences that created Phish up through the current state of the band today. While the pinnacle of the band's career has surpassed us, the historical facts presented are up to date as of early 2021 and should remain mostly unchanged. Phish's most recent original content was released in 2020, with its fifteenth studio album's delivery. The statistics and figures mentioned may have fluctuated with remasters and special releases. The band was active from 1983 through 2004, disbanded, reunited in 2009, and remains active to this day.

Use *Phish - History & Trivia* to evaluate your knowledge of the acclaimed band with rounds of trivia covering various topics throughout the history of Phish. Whether you consider yourself a diehard Phish fan or you're only vaguely familiar with the band, this book will help you assess how much you really know and enlighten you with illuminating and interesting facts.

Let's dive in and see how much you really know about Phish!

CHAPTER 1:

BACK TO THE BEGINNING

TRIVIA TIME!

1. Where was Trey Anastasio Born?

    a. Burlington, Vermont
    b. Princeton, New Jersey
    c. Boston, Massachusetts
    d. Fort Worth, Texas

2. Where did Anastasio grow up?

    a. Burlington, Vermont
    b. Princeton, New Jersey
    c. Boston, Massachusetts
    d. Fort Worth, Texas

3. What was Trey Anastasio's first name at birth?

    a. Trey
    b. Robert
    c. Ernest
    d. Patrick

4. Mike Gordon's father owns which chain of New England convenience stores?

    a. Alltown Fresh

    b. Tedeschi Food Shops

    c. Store 24

    d. Cumberland Farms

5. Where was Jon Fishman born?

    a. Syracuse, New York

    b. Philadelphia, Pennsylvania

    c. Athens, Georgia

    d. Burlington, Vermont

6. Where did Fishman grow up?

    a. Syracuse, New York

    b. Philadelphia, Pennsylvania

    c. Athens, Georgia

    d. Burlington, Vermont

7. Phish is originally from which city?

    a. New York, New York

    b. Los Angeles, California

    c. Burlington, Vermont

    d. Pittsburgh, Pennsylvania

8. Which instruments did the members of Phish play?

    a. Keyboard, vocals, violin, drums, and guitar

    b. Guitar, drums, keyboard, horn, vocals

    c. Vocals, bass, flute, drums, keyboard

    d. Drums, guitar, bass, keyboard, vocals

9. The members of Phish were attending which university when they officially formed the band?

   a. University of Vermont
   b. University of Pittsburgh
   c. University of Delaware
   d. University of Virginia

10. How many lead vocalists does the band have?

   a. One
   b. Two
   c. Three
   d. None

11. What are the names of all of the people who have ever belonged to Phish?

   a. Trey Anastasio, Mike Gordan, Jerry Garcia, Bob Weir, Jon Fishman
   b. Jon Fishman, Page McConnell, Rob McKernan, Trey Anastasio, Mike Gordan
   c. Page McConnell, Jerry Garcia, Mike Gordan, Bob Weir, Rob McKernan
   d. Trey Anastasio, Mike Gordan, Jon Fishman, Page McConnell, Jeff Holdsworth

12. True or False: The lineup of the band has changed a total of three times over the course of 35 years.

13. The band enjoyed the most popularity during which era?

   a. 1980s
   b. 1990s

c. 2000s

d. 2010s

14. "Jam" bands grew in popularity due to which of the following?

   a. Live tours and performances
   b. Word of mouth
   c. The expansion of the internet
   d. The disbanding of many formerly popular rock bands

15. The band started out by doing which of these?

   a. Jam sessions with a few audience members
   b. Live concerts
   c. Releasing their first song
   d. Being signed to their record label

16. True or False: Mike Gordon was the person who brought all of the players together to ultimately create Phish.

17. Where did the group play their first concert?

   a. The University of Vermont
   b. Trey Anastasio's back yard
   c. Princeton, New Jersey
   d. None of the above

18. Phish got their start by opening for which other popular jam band?

   a. The Cure
   b. The Rolling Stones

c. Grateful Dead

d. None of the above

19. True or False: Phish obtained their record deal because lead vocalist Trey Anastasio had connections with members of Grateful Dead.

20. True or False: When the band first started, they played no original content and stuck mostly to covers.

ANSWERS

1. D – Fort Worth, Texas.

2. B – Princeton, New Jersey

3. C – Ernest

4. C – Store 24

5. B – Philadelphia, Pennsylvania

6. A – Syracuse, New York

7. C – Burlington, Vermont

8. D – Drums, guitar, bass, keyboard, and vocals

9. A – University of Vermont

10. A – One. Although all of the members perform vocal duties.

11. D – Trey Anastasio, Mike Gordan, Jon Fishman, Page McConnell, Jeff Holdsworth

12. False – The lineup of the band has changed a total of one time over the course of 35 years.

13. B – 1990s

14. A – Live tours and performances

15. C – Live concerts

16. False - Trey Anastasio was the member of the band who brought all of the players together to ultimately create Phish.

17. A – The University of Vermont

18. D – None of the above

19. False – Phish did not obtain their record deal because lead vocalist Trey Anastasio had connections with members of Grateful Dead.

20. True – When the band first started, they played no original content and stuck mostly to covers.

DID YOU KNOW?

- Although the band's lineup has only officially shifted one time, Anastasio's longtime friend, Marc Daubert, a percussionist, briefly played with the band before quickly leaving in 1985.

- After Trey Anastasio and Jon Fishman became friends and started playing together, the next future Phish member on the scene was Mike Gordon. A talented bassist, Gordon met the trio (Anastasio, Fishman, and Holdsworth) after responding to a "wanted" ad Anastasio had placed around their college.

- The origin of the band's name has been speculated on for years. Many have thought that it's a play on the name of drummer Jon Fishman. Trey confirmed this. However, Fishman argues that it has nothing to do with his last name, and is supposed to be an onomatopoeia for the sound of a plane taking off and lifting into the air.

- The band did not officially call themselves Phish until over a year after their first live concerts at the University of Vermont.

- The fifth and final member of the band joined in 1985. Page McConnell arranged for the band to play a concert at the Goddard College during the spring of 1985. After arranging the set for them, he began playing with the band as a guest, and made his official debut as the band's keyboardist several months after.

- The lead guitarist Trey Anastasio designed the band's official logo shortly after they began referring to themselves as Phish. It consists of the band's name inside of a decorative fish (although the name has nothing to do with actual fish).

- After their first live performance at the Harris Mills Cafeteria in the University of Vermont in 1983, the band only played one other live concert that same year. Following that, the group did not play together for almost a full year.

- Anastasio was briefly suspended from the University of Vermont in 1983 after pulling a prank with a fellow classmate. It was this prank and suspension that contributed to the band's hiatus almost immediately following its formation.

- In the middle of 1986, Trey Anastasio and drummer Jon Fishman transferred to Goddard College, also located in Vermont, at the recommendation of the band's newly appointed keyboardist Page McConnell.

- Following his suspension from the University of Vermont, Trey Anastasio returned to his hometown of Princeton, New Jersey. It was there that he reunited with his childhood friend Tom Marshall. Marshall was a talented lyricist and singer-songwriter. Together, Marshall and Anastasio collaborated and recorded material that would later be featured on the band's first demo tape.

- Following Trey Anastasio and Jon Fishman's transfer to the Goddard College in mid-1986, the band continued playing together and self-distributed six of their own recorded cassette tapes.

- After keyboardist Page McConnell made his official live debut with the band, the group took a brief hiatus for the summer of 1985. During this time, Trey Anastasio and Jon Fishman vacationed in Europe, while McConnell offered to move to Burlington to learn the band's "tools of the trade" from bassist Mike Gordon.

- After the band's brief hiatus following Trey Anastasio's suspension from the University of Vermont, Anastasio returned to Burlington from his hometown of Princeton, New Jersey and resumed playing alongside Fishman, Holdsworth, and Gordan.

CHAPTER 2:

WHO'S WHO AND WHAT'S WHAT

TRIVIA TIME!

1. The band was originally managed by…
   a. Trey Anastasio's music professor
   b. They were self-managed.
   c. Tom Marshall (Trey Anastasio's childhood friend)
   d. None of the above

2. True or False: Marc Daubert is credited with many of the lyrics from the band's repertoire.

3. In which year did Jeff Holdsworth depart from the band?
   a. 1984
   b. 1985
   c. 1983
   d. 1986

4. In addition to being the bassist for Phish, Mike Gordon also handled which other task?

   a. Scheduled their tours
   b. Built the stages and props for their traveling sets
   c. Designed special decals for the band's instruments
   d. Managed all public relations

5. True or False: Anastasio and Fishman were initially hesitant to allow Page McConnell into the band as an official member.

6. How did Jeff Holdsworth and Trey Anastasio know each other?

   a. They grew up in the same town.
   b. They were introduced by a mutual friend.
   c. They were roommates at the University of Vermont.
   d. They attended the same high school but played in different bands.

7. Although the band was established in 1983 and released several albums, Phish did not officially sign to a record label until which year?

   a. 1987
   b. 1986
   c. 1991
   d. 1990

8. Jeff Holdsworth reunited with the band to play a

show in December of which year?

a. 2003
b. 1998
c. 2002
d. 2005

9. Trey Anastasio's music was largely influenced and inspired by...

a. Jerry Garcia
b. Jimi Hendrix
c. Frank Zappa
d. All of the above

10. Where was the band's first official paid gig?

a. A backyard party
b. A local bar
c. A live concert
d. None of the above

11. Which keyboard instruments does Page McConnell play?

a. Piano
b. Organ
c. Synthesizer
d. All of the above

12. True or False: All four members of the band have pursued solo careers and side projects, but only while the band was inactive or on hiatus.

13. What kind of guitar does Trey Anastasio play?

a. Gibson
b. Fender
c. Paul Reed Smith
d. None of the above

14. Gordon used to play a custom-made bass until he switched in 1997. Which bass did he start playing at that point?

a. Modulus Quantum 5
b. American Standard P
c. Mustang PJ
d. ESP LTD B-50

15. What is Amy Skelton's relationship to Phish?

a. Wardrobe manager
b. Set designer
c. First fan
d. Accountant

16. Who was the album *Junta* named after?

a. The Argentinean government
b. The band's manager
c. The band's fans
d. The band's roadies

17. Who has been the bands sound engineer since 2010?

a. Paul Langedoc
b. Susan Rogers
c. Dave Pensado
d. Garry Brown

18. Which company manages Phish?

    a. Red Light Management

    b. Kobalt Music

    c. Crush Management

    d. Velvet Hammer Music and Management Group

19. Shelly Culbertson was a massive force behind the early organization of Phish.net. Which project did she manage basically single-handed?

    a. The WaterWheel Foundation

    b. Dinner and a Movie

    c. Phish Tickets by Mail

    d. LivePhish downloads

20. Who is Leigh Fordham?

    a. A former manager for the band

    b. A former member of the lighting crew

    c. A former roadie

    d. A former sound engineer

ANSWERS

1. B – They were self-managed.

2. False – Tom Marshall is credited with many of the lyrics from the band's repertoire.

3. D – 1986

4. D – Managed all public relations

5. True – Anastasio and Fishman were initially hesitant to allow Page McConnell into the band as an official member.

6. C – They were roommates at the University of Vermont

7. C – 1991

8. A – 2003

9. D – All of the above

10. B – A local bar

11. D – All of the above

12. False – All four members of the band have pursued solo careers and side projects while the band was active.

13. D – None of the above. Anastasio plays a custom hollow-body guitar made by band soundman Paul Langedoc.

14. A – Modulus Quantum 5. He made the final switch at the band's show on March 1, 1997 at Markthalle in Hamburg, Germany.

15. C – Their first fan. The band once held an event at her farm. You can also see Amy's horse on the cover of Hoist.

16. B – The band's manager. Ben "Junta" Hunter was the band's first manager.

17. D – Garry Brown, a former Royal Navy man and sound engineer extraordinaire.

18. A – Red Light Management. They are a company focused on developing the long-term legacy of their clients. The group's roster includes Dave Matthews Band and Alabama Shakes.

19. C – Phish tickets by mail. Her initiative made it more convenient to get tickets and print custom-made graphics while also helping tapers.

20. B – A former member of the lighting crew. Leigh was a particular favorite and appeared as the Bell Boy when the band performed The Who's *Quadrophenia* album. His name also pops up in the opening line of the song "46 Days," which goes, "Leigh Fordham sold me out."

DID YOU KNOW?

- Phish's first gig was dubbed a disaster. Playing for a Reserve Officers' Training Corps (ROTC) dance, they were incorrectly billed as Blackwood Convention. The band got through playing two of their songs before being replaced by Michael Jackson's "Thriller" on the stereo.

- Trey Anastasio learned how to play the guitar during his sophomore year of high school. This is a much older age than many other famous musicians. Anastasio's ability to quickly master the guitar with only a couple years of lessons speaks to his level of natural talent.

- Many fans consider Chris Koruda to be the unofficial "fifth member" of the band. Koruda is the band's lighting director, and became part of the band's regular live concerts and tours in 1988. He is known as an integral part of Phish due to his unique and eccentric lighting skills.

- In addition to being the band's bassist, Mike Gordan is also an advanced banjo player.

- Following the release of their self-produced albums, Phish became acquainted with the audio engineer Paul Languedoc in 1985. During October of 1986, Languedoc became the band's official sound engineer and has been crucial to the successful release of Phish's albums and studio recordings since.

- Phish's "breakthrough," at least in regional terms, is considered to be their performance at the Paradise Rock Club in Boston, Massachusetts. The owners of the club initially refused to let the band play as they had never heard of them before. Phish rented the club for the night, and the entire show sold out. Following this performance, the band began to book bigger and higher-paying gigs.

- Percussionist Marc Daubert and Trey Anastasio attended the same high school. In fact, they were both members of an eleven-person rock band known as Red Tide. Anastasio originally played drums for this band. After most of the members of Red Tide graduated, Anastasio became a self-taught guitarist when the band reformed under a new name.

- After Anastasio was suspended from University, Gordon and Fishman had both joined a cover band called *Dangerous Grapes*. Fishman has stated that he originally liked playing with *Dangerous Grapes* more than Anastasio and Gordan, but he thought Anastasio had a better long-term potential in terms of unique expression and talent.

- The very first gig in which the band was correctly recognized and billed under the name Phish was in the basement of Slade Hall at the University of Vermont. The band played several covers by The Who, as well as an encore rendition of "Proud Mary."

- A man named David Long is credited by Phish as being their "phirst phan." Long was dedicated to attending all of their performances in early 1984 and 1985. He eventually connected the members of Phish with Page McConnell, who later joined the band after organizing a festival where Phish performed.

CHAPTER 3:

SONGS AND SOUNDS

TRIVIA TIME!

1. Why was the band's first official performance together affiliated with the Reserve Officers Training Corp (ROTC)?

    a. Trey Anastasio was close with members of ROTC
    b. Jon Fishman was briefly a member of ROTC
    c. Mike Gordan's dorm was primarily ROTC students
    d. All of the above

2. Phish first officially distributed the band's own original content following which event?

    a. Page McConnell becoming an official member
    b. Trey Anastasio returning from his hometown of Princeton, New Jersey following his suspension from the University of Vermont
    c. Jeff Holdsworth departing from the band after becoming a born-again Christian

d. Jon Fishman deciding to play for the band full-time after graduating college

3. The band's setlist for their first performance at the University of Vermont included which song?

    a. "Long Cool Woman in a Black Dress" by *The Hollies*
    b. "Proud Mary" by *Creedence Clearwater Revival*
    c. "In the Midnight Hour" by *Wilson Pickett*
    d. All of the above

4. Which first collection of songs is regarded as the first "official" Phish album?

    a. *Phish*
    b. *The White Tape*
    c. *Bivouac Juan*
    d. *Junta*

5. After the band was signed to their record label, Elektra Records, they released their...

    a. Third album
    b. Second album
    c. First hit single
    d. Second hit single

6. Artist David Welker created the cover art for which of the band's albums?

    a. *The White Tape*
    b. *Rift*
    c. *A Picture of Nectar*
    d. *Junta*

7. What is the name of the band's second official live-recorded album?

   a. *A Live One*
   b. *Lawn Boy*
   c. *Slip Stich & Pass*
   d. *Hoist*

8. What is the name of the second studio "experiment" created by Anastasio?

   a. *The Man Who Stepped into Yesterday*
   b. *A Man Called Horse*
   c. *Bivouac Juan*
   d. *The White Tape*

9. Copies of the band's first album, *Junta,* were first sold and circulated where?

   a. Record and cassette stores
   b. The radio
   c. Phish's concerts
   d. All of the above

10. True or False: The song titled "Mike's Song" is considered to be the band's signature song.

11. What is the title of the band's second officially recorded and released album?

   a. *Rift*
   b. *Hoist*
   c. *Lawn Boy*
   d. *A Picture of Nectar*

12. The band's song titled "You Enjoy Myself" was first

performed in which year?

    a. 1984

    b. 1986

    c. 1983

    d. 1985

13. True or False: "Mike's Song", a popular song played by the band, is a reference to bass player Mike Gordan.

14. Which song was the band's first to make an appearance on the Billboard Music charts?

    a. "You Enjoy Myself"

    b. "Down with Disease"

    c. "The Lizards"

    d. "Wilson"

15. The band's second official album was released through...

    a. Self-released and distributed

    b. A small independent record label

    c. Elektra Records

    d. None of the above

16. Phish's first live album was released in which year?

    a. 1990

    b. 1993

    c. 1997

    d. 1995

17. The first single for the band's album *Billy Breathes*

was titled which of the following?

   a. "Free"
   b. "Cars Trucks Buses"
   c. "Billy Breathes"
   d. "Prince Caspian"

18. The song titled "Birds of a Feather" was released on which album?

   a. *Rift*
   b. *Hoist*
   c. *The Story of the Ghost*
   d. *Billy Breathes*

19. The band's most recent release (as of early 2021 and not including Live Phish Downloads) was in which year?

   a. 2019
   b. 2020
   c. 2021
   d. 2018

20. What is the name of the band's most successful single on the Billboard charts?

   a. "You Enjoy Myself"
   b. "Birds of a Feather"
   c. "AC/DC Bag"
   d. "Free"

ANSWERS

1. C – Mike Gordan's dorm was primarily ROTC students. It was not an official ROTC event.

2. C – Jeff Holdsworth departing from the band after becoming a born-again Christian

3. D – All of the above

4. D – *Junta*

5. A – Third album

6. B – *Rift*

7. C – *Slip Stich & Pass*

8. A – *The Man Who Stepped into Yesterday*

9. C – Phish's concerts

10. False – The song titled "You Enjoy Myself" is considered to be the band's signature song.

11. C – *Lawn Boy*

12. B – 1986

13. True – "Mike's Song", a popular song played by the band, is a reference to bass player Mike Gordan.

14. B – "Down with Disease"

15. B – A small independent record label (Rough Trade Records of London)

16. D – 1995

17. A – "Free"

18. C – *The Story of the Ghost*

19. B – 2020

20. D – "Free"

DID YOU KNOW?

- *The Man Who Stepped into Yesterday* was originally Trey Anastasio's senior project at Goddard College. It was a nine-song progressive rock concept album that would become the band's second "studio experiment."

- "Chalk Dust Torture" is one of Phish's more popular songs. It was released in 1992 on the album titled *A Picture of Nectar*. The song was written by Tom Marshall. Marshall has stated this work was the last song he wrote using paper and pen before going digital and typing his lyrics on a computer.

- The band's fifth studio album is titled *Hoist*. It was released in March of 1994, and features a variety of guest performers. These include country singer Alison Krauss; banjoist Béla Fleck; Rose Stone, former member of Sly & The Family Stone; trombonist Jonathan Frakes; and the horn section of the musical group Tower of Power.

- Phish's first official music video was filmed in 1994 to promote Phish's first single, "Down With Disease." The music video was featured on the MTV channel briefly, which propelled the song to be the band's first single to hit the Billboard Music Charts.

- In October of 1994, the Dude of Life released his debut album, *Crimes of the Mind*. The album featured all four members of Phish playing backup for Anastasio's friend Steve "The Dude of Life" Pollack.

- Trey Anastasio's college project, *The Man Who Stepped into Yesterday*, was never officially released. However, several bootleg recordings of the experimental concept album have been circulated over the years. Two songs from the album, titled "Wilson" and "Lizards" are often played during the band's concerts.

- Phish debuted several songs during their concerts before they were officially released and featured on their albums. For example, the songs "Prince Caspian," "Billy Breathes," "Theme from the Bottom," "Cars Trucks Buses," "Taste," and "Free" were all played for the first time during Phish's live performances before being officially released on the band's sixth studio album, *Billy Breathes*.

- The band's first album, titled *Junta*, was recorded at Euphoria Sound Studio in Revere, Massachusetts. The studio is now known as Sound & Vision Media.

- Following the finalization of *The Man Who Stepped into Yesterday*, the band began practicing vigorously together with the goal of producing their first album. They practiced together during

31

long jam sessions, which they referred to as "Oh Kee Pah Ceremonies." The name is a reference to a Native American ritual, similar to the one featured in the movie *A Man Called Horse*.

- Phish's eighth album, titled *A Siket Disc*, was initially released through the band's website and mail-order service in 1999. It was later released commercially with Elektra Records in 2000.

- Phish released a cover of the song "Manteca" on their album titled *A Picture of Nectar*. "Manteca" was a popular song released in 1947, co-written by legends Dizzy Gillespie, Chano Pozo, and Gil Fuller. The song is considered to be one of the foundational songs in the genre dubbed "Afro-Cuban Jazz." Phish's cover of the song is shorter and features the melody sung as a nonsense phrase.

- *The Man Who Stepped into Yesterday* relates a story about a fictional universe, referred to as "Gamehendge." The story of Gamehendge and its characters is told over the course of the nine songs on the album, featuring spoken narration in between pieces. The story centers on protagonist Colonel Forbin, a retired colonel from Long Island, New York, who enters Gamehendge and fights the evil villain Wilson to save a document titled "The Helping Friendly Book." The eccentricity of the story paints a picture of the essence of the band.

- Phish's second official album, *Lawn Boy*, originally

released with an independent record label, Absolute A Go Go Records, and was reissued by Elektra Records in 1992.

- Tom Marshall, Anastasio's childhood friend and popular lyricist for the band, also hosts a podcast about Phish, called *Under the Scales*.

- Phish's first demo album, titled *The White Tape*, features an early acapella version of the song "You Enjoy Myself." This version includes all four band members singing the guitar lines that open the song.

- The band's song, "All Things Reconsidered," is featured on their fifth studio album, *Rift*. The song is instrumental and an homage to the news show with a similar title: *All Things Considered*. The radio show airs on National Public Radio, and the song by Phish has been featured on the show several times.

- The cover art, done by David Welker, for the band's album *Rift*, featured images that depicted each of the songs featured on the album, with the exception of "The Horse." Due to this song being excluded from the album art, the band intentionally made the cover of their next album, *Hoist*, feature a horse on its cover.

- Phish's breakthrough single, "Down with Disease," was first played during one of the band's concerts before its official release with Elektra Records in

1994. When it was released on cassette, it was paired with the song "NO2." "NO2" is considered to be a "musique concréte," or a composition of music that uses only recorded sounds as the material for the song. "NO2" features dental drill sound effects.

- "Mike's Song" is the first in a series of three songs known as "Mike's Groove." The other songs in the series are titled "I Am Hydrogen" and "Weekapaug Groove." The song title references bassist Mike Gordon because for many years it was the only song he had ever written.

- The band's *The Story of the Ghost* album was mainly comprised of Phish's long improvisational jam sessions. The band took their favorite pieces of their recorded sessions and added Tom Marshall's lyrics where they saw the best fit. Additional pieces from these jam sessions were later featured on the album *A Siket Disc*.

- In 2000, Elektra Records released a collection of songs recorded together by Trey Anastasio and lyricist Tom Marshall in 1997 on an eight-track tape. The collection was titled *Trampled by Lambs and Pecked by the Dove*.

- The band's first live album, titled *A Live One*, was named in response to a fan asking the question, "When are you gonna put out a live one?"

- For Phish's second album released with Elektra

Records, the song titled "Fee," originally from the album *Junta*, was featured as a bonus track. The second album was titled *Lawn Boy*, after the song written by Anastasio and Marshall of the same title.

- Phish's signature song, "You Enjoy Myself," is a structured piece composed of several sections, each named separately by the band's devoted fanbase. Some of the titles for the sections include "Pre-Nirvana," "Nirvana," "The Note," "The Second Note," and "The Charge." One particular section of the song beloved by fans is the "vocal jam" in which all of the band members sing together, harmonizing and performing acapella.

- *Farmhouse* was the ninth studio album released by the band with Elektra Records. All of the songs included on the album were circulated during the band's concerts and live performances before appearing on the official release. The songs were mainly written by Trey Anastasio and Tom Marshall, but also included contributions from Tony Markellis, Russ Lawton, and Scott Herman.

- Guitarist Jeff Holdsworth, a former member of Phish, contributed two compositions titled "Camel Walk" and "Possum." Both were featured in the 2004 reunion concert with all four members of the band and Holdsworth.

CHAPTER 4:

WILD PERFORMANCES

TRIVIA TIME!

1. How long did Phish perform with a five-piece lineup after Page McConnell joined the band?

    a. One year
    b. Six months
    c. Ten months
    d. Two years

2. True or False: The band went on their first national tour by becoming participants in the H.O.R.D.E (Horizons of Rock Developing Everywhere) Festival in 1992.

3. In which year did Phish announce their breakup?

    a. 2002
    b. 2000
    c. 2004
    d. 2005

4. How many people were in the crowd when Phish reunited at the Hampton Coliseum?

    a. 10,000
    b. 13,000
    c. 16,000
    d. 12,000

5. On average, how many concerts per year has Phish played in the years they were actively touring?

    a. 20
    b. 30
    c. 50
    d. 70

6. With which of the following bands has Phish performed?

    a. Radiohead
    b. Red Hot Chili Peppers
    c. Santana
    d. All of the above

7. True or False: In the summer of 2017, Phish played thirteen consecutive concerts at Madison Square Garden.

8. The band ended 1992 with a New Year's Eve performance in which city?

    a. Princeton, New Jersey
    b. Boston, Massachusetts
    c. Plainfield, Vermont
    d. None of the above

9. The band toured with which musical group in 1991?

    a. Santana

    b. Tower of Power

    c. Spin Doctors

    d. Giant Country Horns

10. How did the band communicate with the audience during their live performances?

    a. The lyrics in their songs

    b. Instructions distributed prior to the start of the concert

    c. Through a secret language the band created alongside their fanbase

    d. Instructions displayed during the concert

11. The band has played several shows in which European country?

    a. Germany

    b. Finland

    c. Sweden

    d. None of the above

12. Which live album features the entirety of the band's live performances from November 21 and November 22, 1998?

    a. *A Live One*

    b. *The Siket Disc*

    c. *Hampton Comes Alive*

    d. *Live Phish Volume 11*

13. The band's tour in fall of 1997 was referred to as which of the following?

    a. The Fall of 1997 Tour
    b. Island Tour
    c. Big Ball Jam
    d. Phish Destroys America

14. How many concerts has Phish performed at Madison Square Garden?

    a. 54
    b. 64
    c. 74
    d. 104

15. True or False: The band has long emphasized digital recording methods and media coverage of their live performances.

16. Phish's second Festival was held during which year?

    a. 1996
    b. 1997
    c. 1998
    d. 1999

17. In Glen Falls, NY on October 31, 1994, the band donned their first Halloween "Musical Costume," which involves them playing another band's album from start to finish. Which album did they perform that night?

a. The Beatles – *White Album*
b. Beach Boys – *Pet Sounds*
c. Talking Heads – *Remain in Light*
d. The Who – *Quadrophenia*

18. In 1995, Phish asked fans to select which record they would play in its entirety on Halloween. However, they did not end up playing the album that got the most votes, deciding to go with The Who's *Quadrophenia* instead. Which album was actually chosen?

a. Jimi Hendrix – *Are You Experienced*
b. Yes – *Fragile*
c. Frank Zappa – *Joe's Garage*
d. Pink Floyd – *Dark Side of the Moon*

19. During the 2013 New Year's Eve performance, where did the band put their microphones as a tribute to their early days?

a. On chain link fence
b. On hockey sticks
c. On top of the drums
d. Dangling from the ceiling

20. During their New Year's Eve shows, Phish likes to combine songs with the traditional New Year's Eve song "Auld Lang Syne." Which song did they use the most often for this purpose?

a. "Down with Disease"
b. "You Enjoy Myself"
c. "Chalk Dust Torture"

d. Slave to the Traffic Light

ANSWERS

1. B – Six months

2. False – The band had been touring nationally for two years prior to that tour.

3. C – 2004

4. B – 13,000

5. C – 50

6. D – All of the above

7. True – In the summer of 2017, Phish played thirteen consecutive concerts at Madison Square Garden. They returned for four more shows there at the end of the year.

8. B – Boston, Massachusetts

9. D – *Giant Country Horns*

10. C – Through a secret language the band created alongside their fanbase

11. A – Germany

12. C – *Hampton Comes Alive*

13. D – "Phish Destroys America"

14. B – 64

15. False – The band did not emphasize the digital recording and media coverage of their live performances.

16. B – 1997

17. A – The Beatles – *White Album*. The band let the fans vote for the album they wanted, which they did through good old-fashioned snail mail. Phish had never played any of the songs on the album before, aside from "Piggies," which they had played about a decade earlier.

18. C – Frank Zappa – *Joe's Garage*. The band decided to avoid doing Joe's Garage for two reasons. First, it involved a lot of overdubs and sound effects that would have been hard to recreate live. In addition, Frank had asked that some of the songs on the album never be performed again.

19. B – Hockey sticks. They had used those in their first show because they did not have mic stands. The band also performed the set atop an old touring van. Needless to say, this was a weird scene for Madison Square Garden.

20. A – "Down with Disease." They have combined the two songs four times on New Year's Eve. The last time was in 2011.

DID YOU KNOW?

- *Phish*'s second live album release, titled *Slip Stich and Pass*, features recordings from their live performances in Hamburg, Germany at the Markthalle Hall convention center in March of 1997.

- The band created a collaboration referred to as "Big Ball Jam" and introduced it to audiences in 1992. The collaboration consisted of each of the four band members throwing a large beach ball into the audience. The audience would then toss and hit the beach balls back and forth, and the band members would play a note each time they saw the ball being hit.

- Phish's release of all of their shows on the *Island Tour* was their first release to be simultaneously available in a digital as well as a physical format.

- The band would often communicate and interact with the audience during their live performances. Trey Anastasio would "cue" the audience by playing something that resembled *The Simpsons* theme song, and in return the audience would reply with "D'oh!" —an imitation of the character Homer Simpson.

- In April of 1998, members of the band played the second show at the new club, named Higher

44

Ground, in Winooski, Vermont. This performance was notable for its inclusion of eight-foot fluorescent tubes on the stage set. During this performance, costumed dancers were hoisted above the stage using cables, props like a huge cardboard cactus were used, and Phish debuted new material by the band.

- After the passing of Grateful Dead lead guitarist and vocalist Jerry Garcia, many fans of the band (known as "Deadheads") began following Phish. It is because of Garcia's death that Phish's concert attendance greatly increased in the late 1990s.

- The band's second studio album, titled *Lawn Boy*, was recorded a year previous to its official release with Absolute A Go Go Records. It was first recorded when Phish won a battle of the bands contest hosted by sound engineer Dan Archer. The prize was time in his studio, Archer Studios.

- The earliest performance of Gamehendge, the story of the fictional universe created by the band's lead guitarist, Trey Anastasio, was in 1985. Phish played a song from the story, titled "McGrupp and the Watchful Hosemasters," at a concert in Burlington, Vermont.

- In the summer of 1992, Phish toured Europe with Violent Femmes, an American folk punk rock band from Milwaukee, Wisconsin. Following this tour, Carlos Santana invited Phish to open for him.

- In April of 1999, Phish played alongside the Grateful Dead. The two bands held a joint concert together at the Warfield Theater in San Francisco, California. Phish played with Phil Lesh, Steve Kimock, and John Molo, all members of Grateful Dead.

- The band's well-remembered Island Tour was a four-night event with two shows held at the Nassau Coliseum in Uniondale, New York and another two at the Providence Civic Center in Providence, Rhode Island. The tour is highly regarded by fans due to its inclusion of the musical genre dubbed "cow-funk" by Trey Anastasio.

- On New Year's Day in Big Cypress, Florida, the band played a set that lasted over eight hours. This concert took place in 1999 around the time of the Y2K scare. The band dedicated this concert to their loyal fanbase and played from midnight to sunrise for 85,000 people.

- Phish is incredibly dedicated to never playing the same set twice. In 2017, Phish played thirteen consecutive concerts at Madison Square Garden. With 237 songs played, the band never repeated the same song twice.

- In one of the band's 1996 concerts, while playing the song titled "Catapult," Mike Gordan performed an interpretive dance incorporating colorful scarves for the audience.

- One of the weirder elements of a Phish performance was noted during the Coventry festival, when in the middle of the band's set, over 40,000 fans walked over a plank to avoid sinking into the mud. Although unintentional, many fans regard it as one of the stranger shows put on by the band.

CHAPTER 5:

TV, MOVIES, RADIO & MORE

TRIVIA TIME!

1. The band released a six-minute documentary to promote which album?

    a. *Rift*
    b. *Hoist*
    c. *Billy Breathes*
    d. *A Live One*

2. The band made their debut on national television in which year?

    a. 1988
    b. 1990
    c. 1996
    d. 1994

3. The band officially licensed their name, Phish, to which popular company?

    a. Ben & Jerry's

b. MTV

c. Nabisco

d. Blockbuster

4. The band broadcasted a live performance on the internet for the first time in which year?

    a. 1995

    b. 1999

    c. 1997

    d. 1996

5. True or False: Page McConnell directed the band's first official music video.

    a. Phish achieved their largest television audience in which year?

    b. 1999

    c. 2000

    d. 2002

    e. 2004

6. The band appeared in an episode of *The Simpsons* in which year?

    a. 2000

    b. 2003

    c. 2002

    d. 2004

7. True or False: Famous movie actor Tom Hanks has joined the band on stage.

8. Which of the band's festivals was recorded and

released on DVD?

- a. Coventry
- b. Big Ball Jam
- c. The Show
- d. It

9. *Phish: The Biography* was written by which of the following people?

- a. A Phish fan
- b. Trey Anastasio
- c. Tom Marshall
- d. None of the above

10. Which of the following is NOT the title of a documentary about the band?

- a. *Tracking*
- b. *Phish: Live in Brooklyn*
- c. *Between Me and My Mind*
- d. *The Show*

11. The first podcast about the band ran during which time period?

- a. 2008-2012
- b. 2011-2014
- c. 2013-2016
- d. 2017-2019

12. In which year did a documentary about Trey appear at the Tribeca Film Festival?

- a. 2015

b. 2016

c. 2017

d. 2019

13. True or False: Mike Gordan directed one of the documentaries about the band.

14. Which radio platform launched an exclusively Phish music station?

    a. iHeartRadio
    b. Spotify
    c. Sirius XM
    d. Urban Radio Broadcasting

15. True or False: The band performed during the half-time show of Super Bowl IX.

16. What was, without a doubt, the most emotional part of the documentary *Between Me and My Mind*?

    a. The birth of Trey's daughter
    b. Trey's relationship with his mother
    c. Trey dealing with the fallout of his drug problem
    d. The death of Trey's childhood friend

17. Phish first appeared on the David Letterman show on December 30, 1994. Which song did they play?

    a. "Free"
    b. "Bathtub Gin"
    c. "Stash"
    d. "Chalk Dust Torture"

18. In 1998, the band played what was possibly its best televised set on the show *Sessions at West 54th*. Which network did it air on?

    a. PBS
    b. NBC
    c. MTV
    d. CBS

19. True or False: ABC news showed the countdown to midnight at the legendary Phish New Year's Eve show (and technically new millennium show) at Big Cypress.

ANSWERS

1. B – *Hoist*. The documentary was titled *Tracking*.

2. D – 1994

3. A – Ben & Jerry's

4. C – 1997

5. False – Mike Gordon directed the band's only official music video.

6. B – 2000

7. C – 2002

8. False – It was a prank.

9. D – It

10. A – A *Phish* fan

11. D – *The Show*

12. B – 2011-2014

13. D – 2019

14. True – Mike Gordon directed one of the documentaries about the band.

15. C – SiriusXM

16. False – The band *did not* perform during the half-time show of Super Bowl IX.

17. D – The death of Trey's childhood friend. Chris "C-Cot" Cottrell died of adrenal cancer in January of 2018 during the making of the film.

18. D – "Chalk Dust Torture." The next day the band played Madison Square Garden for the first time. Talk about conquering the Big Apple!

19. A – PBS. The televised set was pretty short and only included three songs. Luckily, the set of eleven songs is available on YouTube. It includes ten originals and a stellar cover of Neil Young's "Albuquerque."

20. False – ABC tuned in a bit after midnight because of the incredible buzz the show was getting. They broadcast Phish as they launched into a rendition of "Heavy Things." Knowing the song was being televised, Trey asked the crowd to avoid clapping but instead chant "cheesecake" angrily to confuse the innocent viewers at home.

DID YOU KNOW?

- Following the finale of the band's Summer Tour in 2000, Phish travelled to Austin, Texas to record an episode of *Austin City Limits*. The popular television show is a long-running concert series that records live performances of musicians from all genres.

- Phish has placed so much emphasis on their live performances that recordings of their concerts are consistently in high demand. In December of 2002, the band launched their very own website, LivePhish, where fans can purchase soundboard recordings of their favorite performances.

- Phish has only appeared on the popular show *Saturday Night Live* once. After the band released their tenth studio album, titled *Round Room*, the band appeared on the show and performed their new song "46 Days." They also participated in two different comedy skits.

- After the band announced their hiatus was over in 2002, they revealed that their grand return performance would be during New Year's Eve at Madison Square Garden. During this performance, keyboardist Page McConnell's brother was introduced as famous actor Tom Hanks in an attempt to prank the audience. Funnily enough, the prank was somewhat successful. After singing a part of their song "Wilson," several media outlets inaccurately reported that Tom Hanks had performed with the band.

- "Birds of a Feather" appears in a 1998 episode of the popular teen drama *Dawson's Creek*. The song was featured several weeks before the band's release of their seventh studio album, titled *The Story of the Ghost*.

- The concert documentary *Phish: Live in Brooklyn* was released in 2006. The concert was performed in 2004 at the minor league baseball stadium, Key Span Park, in Brooklyn, New York. It was the first show of what they had promoted as their "final tour."

- In the summer of 2004, the band had a historic performance on the marquee of the Ed Sullivan Theater in New York City. The show was part of a surprise set orchestrated by *The Late Show with David Letterman*. Fans of the band and passersby enjoyed a seven-song set as part of an impromptu performance organized as part of their "farewell" tour before taking their second hiatus in 2004.

- Even though the band was initially hesitant to release a music video — as they thought it would take away from their emphasis on live performances — they released one in the summer of

1994. The music video was directed by bassist Mike Gordan, who has a degree in Filmmaking.

- In 1995, one of the band's songs appeared in the popular animated television show *Beavis and Butt-Head*. "Down with Disease" is credited on the soundtrack of the episode titled "Bad Dog."

- After the COVID-19 pandemic brought government shutdowns and months of quarantine, the band hosted free weekly "Dinner and a Movie" webcasts of their previously recorded performances every Tuesday evening.

- In 2000, the documentary titled *Bittersweet Motel* was released. It focused on Phish's 1997 summer and fall tours, with exclusive footage of their 1998 tour in Europe. The film also includes footage of the band's performances at "The Great Went," a large music festival in Maine that attracted an audience of 70,000.

CHAPTER 6:

SOLO MOMENTS & CAREERS

TRIVIA TIME!

1. Mike Gordon can also play which of the following instruments?

    a. Banjo
    b. Piano
    c. Guitar
    d. All of the above

2. True or False: The musical collaboration and project titled *Bivouac Juan* included all four of the original band members.

3. Trey Anastasio released his first album without the help of his childhood friend Tom Marshall in which year?

    a. 2000
    b. 2005
    c. 2003
    d. 2006

4. How many solo albums has Gordon released (not including collaborations with Leo Kottke)?

    a. Three
    b. Four
    c. Five
    d. Seven

5. What did Jon Fishman study in college?

    a. Music
    b. Filmmaking
    c. Business
    d. Engineering

6. True or False: Page McConnell has never released a solo album.

7. Which of the following is one of Anastasio's side projects?

    a. Trey Anastasio Band
    b. Ghosts of the Forest
    c. Oysterhead
    d. All of the above

8. Years after being signed to Elektra Records, the band created their own label under which name?

    a. Phish Records
    b. JEMP Records
    c. Anastasio Records
    d. None of the above

9. Gordon has his own separate touring band with

which fellow member of Phish?

    a. Trey Anastasio

    b. Page McConnell

    c. Jon Fishman

    d. None of the above

10. Fishman began hosting his own radio show during which year?

    a. 2015

    b. 2016

    c. 2017

    d. 2019

11. The band's lyricist Tom Marshall fronts a rock band by the name of…

    a. Osiris

    b. Bivouac Juan

    c. The McLovins

    d. Amfibian

12. Which of the following was written by McConnell?

    a. "Cars Trucks Buses"

    b. "Windy City"

    c. "I Been Around"

    d. All of the above

13. Fishman emerged from "semi-retirement" in which year?

    a. 2005

    b. 2007

c. 2009

d. 2010

14. Anastasio released his first solo album in which year?

   a. 1996
   b. 1999
   c. 2000
   d. 1998

15. In 2015, Trey was invited to play with Grateful Dead for a series of concerts called Fare Thee Well. Where were these shows held?

   a. San Francisco, California
   b. Chicago, Illinois
   c. Portland, Oregon
   d. Atlanta, Georgia

16. How long did Anastasio spend preparing for the Fare Thee Well shows?

   a. He flew in the day before and rehearsed with the band.
   b. A week
   c. A month
   d. Five months

17. True or False: Anastasio said that he was disappointed by his time playing with Grateful Dead.

18. Which character on the show *The Office* claimed to have played with Anastasio?

a. Robert "Broccoli Rob" Blatt
b. David Wallace
c. Todd Packer
d. Brian the Sound Guy

ANSWERS

1. D – All of the above

2. False – The musical collaboration and project titled *Bivouac Juan did not* include all four of the original band members.

3. B – 2005

4. C – Five

5. D – Engineering

6. False – Page McConnell *has* released a solo album.

7. D – All of the above

8. B – JEMP Records

9. D – None of the above

10. C – 2017

11. D – *Amfibian*

12. D – All of the above

13. B – 2007

14. D – 1998

15. B – Chicago, Illinois. The shows were held at Soldier Field.

16. D – Five months. Trey could not have taken this job more seriously. He shelved all of his obligations for

Phish and the Trey Anastasio Band. His goal was to learn Jerry Garcia's iconic tone and style inside and out.

17. False – Very false. He had an amazing experience. Phish is known for its long improvisational style. However, he discovered Grateful Dead was on a whole other level. He recalled, "I love to jam. I love to jam long. But even for me, the time would come when I'd think, 'This is too noodle-y. Let's play the next song.' I would do something, a lick, that gently alluded to it. Then Phil [Lesh] would look over at me and put his hand up, like, 'What's your rush, dude?'"

18. A – Robert "Broccoli Rob" Blatt. The character performs a Vermont state milk lobby song titled "Calci-YUM!" with Anastasio.

DID YOU KNOW?

- After studying Filmmaking & Communications at the University of Vermont, despite having a music-oriented career, Mike Gordon was able to put his degree to work. In 2001, Gordon's first feature film premiered in select theaters. Titled *Outside Out*, the film starred Jimi Stout, Col. Bruce Hampton, Ashley Scott Shamp, and Gordan. The film is about a teenager who begins to take guitar lessons and is sent to military school by his parents. The main character then meets the guitarist of an eccentric country group. The film is overall described as being outlandish and bizarre.

- Page McConnell started his own band in 2001. The group included McConnell, Oteil Burbridge from the Allman Brothers Band, and Russell Batiste from The Meters. The group became known as Vida Blue, after the Major League Baseball player.

- In addition to his five solo studio albums, Gordon has also released three albums with acoustic guitarist Leo Kottke. Kottke is known for the unique combination of blues, jazz, and folk music elements that make up his finger-picking style.

- From April 1999 to September 2000, Anastasio and McConnell were members of the rotating musical group known as Phil Lesh and Friends. Anastasio returned in 2006. The group was created by Phil Lesh, the former bassist for Grateful Dead. Other members of the group have included Warren Haynes, Derek Trucks, Jimmy Herring, and Robben Ford. Anastasio played guitar for the band, while McConnell played the keyboard.

- Fishman is adored by fans for his quirky attributes during Phish's performances. He is known for playing his Electrolux vacuum cleaner on the band's tours, as well as wearing a muumuu featuring a donut print. In past interviews, Fishman has admitted to taking acid before performing in the earlier days of the band.

- McConnell has also worked as a session musician for the comedy rock group Tenacious D, which was founded by Jack Black and Kyle Gass in 1994.

- In 2005, Anastasio was part of a trio of musicians known as SerialPod. The trio consisted of Anastasio, Gordon, and Bill Kruetzmann of Grateful Dead. The group played together in Asheville, North Carolina at the 14th annual Warren Haynes Christmas Jam. They played a medley of Phish and Grateful Dead songs, as well as several covers of songs by Nirvana and Jimi Hendrix.

- In addition to *Outside Out*, Gordan released his second film in 2002. Titled *Rising Low*, the film is a documentary recounting the life and career of bassist Allen Woody. The film was shot not long after the tragic death of the founding member of Gov't Mule and bassist for the Allman Brothers Band. In the film, Gordon interviews Woody's bandmates and family to discuss his success and style of playing.

- While Phish took its official hiatus, McConnell also took a hiatus from the entire music industry. He returned in 2007 with a solo album titled *Page McConnell*, released with Sony BMG's Legacy Recordings. McConnell stated that he chose to go with Legacy Records because he felt that they would push his album through to a larger audience. His goal was to expose as many people as possible to his music and style.

- Fishman, is very particular about the type of drumsticks he uses for which occasion. He most regularly uses Vic Firth drumsticks, a company known for making quality percussion sticks and mallets. Fishman has stated his "perfect pair" of drumsticks is the Peter Erskine Ride Stick and the American Classic 55A. For practice, Fishman uses TG12 sticks.

- One of Anastasio's notable contributions to music outside of Phish was his appearance on the album *True Love* by Toots and the Maytals. Released in 2004, the album featured many other notable musicians, including Willie Nelson, Eric Clapton,

Jeff Beck, Gwen Stefani, Ben Harper, Bonnie Raitt, Manu Chao, The Roots, Keith Richards, Toots Hibbart, Paul Douglas, Jackie Jackson, Ken Boothe, and The Skatalites. Specifically, Anastasio is featured on the song "Sweet and Dandy."

- Fishman is currently a drummer and travelling member of the Burlington, Vermont comedy group Touchpants. The group consists of Fishman, Colby Dix, Chris Friday, and Aram Bedrosian. Touchpants often performs directly after and sometimes in between the sets of Phish's performances and concerts.

- Among the collection of Anastasio's side projects is the band known as Oysterhead. The group is an American-based rock band that features Anastasio on guitar, Les Claypool of Primus on bass, and Stewart Copeland of The Police on drums. Anastasio and Claypool also provide vocals for the band. Oysterhead was formed when, in April of 2000, the marketing and event company known as Superfly Presents made the request that Les Claypool put together a musical group to perform at the New Orleans Jazz Fest.

- In the fall of 2010, Tom Marshall collaborated with the rock/jam band known as The McLovins. Together, Marshall and The McLovins co-wrote the song "Cohesive," which was then recorded with Anthony Krizan at Krizan's Sonic Boom Studios.

- Fishman briefly played with a band he co-founded in 1997, Pork Tornado. The band consisted of Fishman on drums, Dan Archer on guitar, Aaron Hershey on bass, and Phil Abair on keyboards. All members of the band also occasionally offered vocals. The musical group was categorized as a country-western and rock band. They played original content as well as cover songs. In 2002, the band released their only album, self-titled Pork Tornado. Following the release of their album, they embarked on a small tour, mainly on the Eastern side of the United States. After this, there was a long period of inactivity. The band briefly reunited in 2013 for a show in Burlington, Vermont.

- In July of 2007, McConnell was a headliner at the High Sierra Music Festival in Quincy, California. He played alongside his touring band, which included Jared Slomoff on a variety of instruments, Adam Zimmon on guitar, Rob O'Dea on bass, and Gabe Jarrett on the drums.

CHAPTER 7:

GENRES AND INFLUENCES

TRIVIA TIME!

1. Which of the following contributed to Phish's growth in popularity and number of fans?

    a. Their incorporation of internet sales and livestreams
    b. Word of mouth
    c. Jerry Garcia (of Grateful Dead) passing in 1995
    d. All of the above

2. The band began to include "barbershop quartet" sections into their shows in which year?

    a. 1990
    b. 1992
    c. 1993
    d. 1994

3. The term used to describe their music, "cow-funk," was originally coined by which member?

    a. Jon Fishman
    b. Trey Anastasio

c. Page McConnell

d. Mike Gordon

4. Anastasio has commented that Phish's first couple of albums can be closely compared to the style of which band?

   a. Grateful Dead
   b. Santana
   c. King Crimson
   d. Yes

5. The band stopped performing Grateful Dead cover songs in which period?

   a. Early 1990s
   b. Mid 1980s
   c. Early 2000s
   d. Late 1980s

6. The band's very first hit single that reached the Billboard Music charts was classified in which category?

   a. Alternative Rock
   b. Mainstream Rock
   c. Punk Rock
   d. New Wave

7. Which band that inspired Phish has also toured with them?

   a. King Crimson
   b. Yes

    c. Allman Brothers Band

    d. Santana

8. In 1998, *Rolling Stone* named Phish which of these?

    a. The most influential alternative band of the '80s

    b. The most important rock band of the '90s

    c. The most popular rock band of the '80s

    d. The most influential rock band of the '90s

9. The band's popular events inspired the creation of which music festival?

    a. New Orleans Jazz & Heritage Festival

    b. The Clifford Ball

    c. Camp Oswego

    d. Bonnaroo Music Festival

10. The band's fans are lovingly most commonly referred to as which of the following?

    a. Phishies

    b. Phishes

    c. Phans

    d. Phishheads

11. True or False: Jazz fusion is one of Phish's many influences.

12. The band heavily influences and contributes to which industry?

    a. Musical tourism

    b. Instrumental production

c. Song design

d. Vocal technique

13. In the version of "Mike's Song" on *Slip Stitch and Pass*, the band quotes the classic Doors song "The End." However, instead of the oedipal statements in the original live version, Phish replaced it with which line?

   a. "Mother, I want to make you breakfast. Dad, I want to borrow the car."

   b. "Mother, I want to buy you flowers. Dad, I want to play catch."

   c. "Mother, I want to take you to the zoo. Dad, I want to make you blue."

   d. "Mother, I want to do your dishes. Dad, I want to pay your bills."

14. Page McConnell has a Keytar that was previously owned by which R&B icon?

   a. Tina Turner

   b. James Brown

   c. Luther Vandross

   d. Van Morrison

15. Which song has Phish covered the most?

   a. Argent – "Hold Your Head Up"

   b. Led Zeppelin – "Good Times, Bad Times"

   c. The Rolling Stones – "Loving Cup"

   d. Talking Heads – "Cities"

16. True or False. Bruce Springsteen appeared with the

band at the Bonnaroo Festival.

17. Which of the following people showed up unannounced to jam with the band at a show in Continental Airlines Arena in East Rutherford in February 2003?

    a. B.B. King
    b. Eric Clapton
    c. Buddy Guy
    d. Bonnie Raitt

18. In 1994, while in Bloomington, Indiana, the band played a famous bluegrass set in which unconventional location?

    a. On the roof of a building
    b. A sauna
    c. A parking lot
    d. A gym

19. Which bluegrass great joined the band for a set at the Camp Oswego festival in 1999?

    a. Alison Krauss
    b. Del McCoury
    c. Mac Wiseman
    d. Ricky Scaggs

20. In 1996, the band played the New Orleans Jazz & Heritage Festival for the first time. Which former musical partner of experimental jazz legend Sun Ra played with them?

    a. Yahya Abdul-Majid

b. Michael Ray
c. Taylor Richardson
d. Damon Choice

ANSWERS

1. D – All of the above

2. C – 1993

3. B – Trey Anastasio

4. D – *Yes*

5. D – Late 1980's

6. C – Both A and B

7. B – Mainstream Rock

8. D – *Santana*

9. B – The most important rock band of the '90s

10. D – Bonnaroo Music Festival

11. D – Phishheads

12. A – Musical tourism

13. A – "Mother, I want to make you breakfast. Dad, I want to borrow the car."

14. B – James Brown. Page is known for whipping it out during his amazing solos on covers of the Edgar Winter Group's "Frankenstein."

15. A – Argent – "Hold Your Head Up." The band has played it no fewer than 308 times since debuting it on August 21, 1987. However, they have never

completed the entire song. The song worked its way into the setlist as part of a private joke. Fishman despised the tune. Just to annoy him, the other members would launch into the song during rehearsal. He hated it so much that he would sometimes storm out of practice. Taking the joke even further, they began playing it in shows when Fish was supposed to sing a number.

16. True – The Boss played the Festival in 2009. Phish played the day after Springsteen, and he stayed just to catch their show. The band invited him on stage, and they closed out the set together. They ripped through versions of soul standard "Mustang Sally," and Bruce's hits "Bobby Jean" and "Glory Days."

17. A – B.B. King. The blues legend didn't show up to make a brief cameo. The King of the blues rolled up his sleeves and jammed with Phish for almost an hour, playing "Everyday I Have the Blues," "The Thrill Is Gone," and "Rock Me Baby." When B.B. passed away in May 2015, Anastasio posted the following message: "It's literally impossible to overstate B.B. King's influence on every single electric guitarist who followed in his path. All of us who have ever bent a note owe him an enormous debt of gratitude."

18. C – A parking lot. The band played a twelve-song set focused on country and bluegrass. Anastasio played both guitar and fiddle, Gordon played the

banjo, Fishman played mandolin, and McConnell was on upright bass. As they played "Will the Circle be Unbroken," the tour bus began to honk for the band to pack up their stuff and leave.

19. B – Del McCoury. In return, Phish played McCoury's Delfest in 2013. The band often play his classic "Beauty of My Dreams." Anastasio has said that the band often played Del's Blue *Side of Town* album in their van.

20. B – Michael Ray. He played on "Cars Trucks Buses." The band also did the first two verses of "Wolfman's Brother" in an acapella version.

DID YOU KNOW?

- The digital age brought an opportunity for huge growth for the band, its following, and its exposure to the public. The advancement and access of the internet and its many features, including mostly websites and live streaming, greatly influenced Phish's rise to fame.

- In a quote from Richard Gehr's *The Phish Book*, Anastasio explains that the music style they play focuses more on groove elements than funk. He says, "Good funk, real funk, is not played by four white guys from Vermont..." The style of "funk" originated from African-American communities in the mid 1960s. Anastasio goes on to explain that what they do is "more like cow-funk," a reference to the abundant number of cows in Vermont. In essence, Anastasio is showing his respect for the genre and its origin.

- One of Trey Anastasio's mentors is composer Ernie Stires. Stires and Anastasio formed a relationship shortly after Anastasio had transferred to Goddard College. Stires had moved to Vermont in 1967 and worked for many years as a volunteer teaching music and compositional skills to youth. Trey Anastasio was one of his students, and Stires taught him composition, theory, and music arrangement.

In a past interview, Anastasio has stated that he "owes it all to Stires."

- Gordon's musical influence shows through in the band. He is inspired by bluegrass and calypso music. Gordon and drummer Jon Fishman are both Jewish, which has influenced the band to produce several covers of traditional Jewish songs, some of which include "Yerushalayim Shel Zahav" and "Avinu Malkeinu."

- Several of the band's songs can be categorized as compositions. For Phish, these are songs that contain elements of music that are "untraditional." Oftentimes, this includes improvisational songs that have a longer duration than the average. The band's signature song, "You Enjoy Myself," can be considered a composition due to its employment of such things as staccatos and fugues.

- One genre that has heavily influenced the band is psychedelic rock. This particular style of rock is centered around the culture of hallucinogenic drugs, specifically LSD. The genre emerged in the 1960s and focused on creating music that gave people a similar feeling to being on drugs.

- Although Phish is often compared to the other well-known jam band, Grateful Dead, several of the band members have spoken about trying to distance themselves from the constant comparison. Anastasio made this statement: "When we first came into the awareness of the media, it would always be the Dead or Zappa they'd compare us to. All of these bands I love, you know? But I got very sensitive about it." The band recognizes that perhaps without Grateful Dead, Phish would not have come about, but Phish has still attempted to distance themselves from the juxtaposition of the two musical groups.

- The original inspiration for Fishman to use his Electrolux vacuum cleaner as an instrument came from Fishman's mother. When Fishman was young, his mother took a different approach on disciplining her child when it came to his use of profane language. Fishman said, she "sucked all those f-words right down her Hoover. I used to bring up the vacuum cleaner to make her feel guilty." Fishman later added, "but now she just asks, 'Aren't you glad I did it?'"

- Another large genre of music that has influenced Phish's music is bluegrass. Bluegrass is a style of music that emerged out of the Appalachian area in the 1940's. The name "bluegrass" is a nod to Bill Monroe and the Blue Grass Boys, a group whose leading man, William Smith Monroe, is considered to be the "father of bluegrass." The genre is similar to country music, but is different in that it is often played using acoustic stringed instruments. Within the style, it is common for the instruments to "take turns," each playing the melody and improvising to add some flare.

- Phish lyrics are often, strangely enough, influenced by nothing at all. The words are simply arbitrary and nonsensical. This is done purposefully to force the audience into confusion and make them focus on the sound of the music instead of just hearing the words. Trey Anastasio began this style of nonsense during his senior project at Goddard College. Part of his thesis was that "people take lyrics too seriously."

- Another popular genre that has influenced the music and songs of Phish is progressive rock. Progressive rock contains several distinct elements. Some of these elements include poetic lyrics, advanced technology utilized for new sounds, and turning music into "art." This era experienced a shift of focus from the stage into the studio where the music was created.

- There were several factors that contributed to the band's hiatus beginning in the year 2002. The largest driving factor was fear that the band's success was overshadowing their goal of making unique music. Following their return, Phish made the decision to limit their touring in order to get "back to basics."

- The Phish fan community is very close-knit and loyal to the band. Fishman has stated that their live performances drove the close relationship between the band and its fans, "creating that communal spirit." It is this communal spirit that has made the success of Phish span several decades.

CHAPTER 8:

PERSONAL LIVES

TRIVIA TIME!

1. In 2007, Anastasio was pulled over by the police. Which drug was in his possession at the time?

   a. Xanax
   b. Heroin
   c. Percocet
   d. Vicodin

2. What happened to the charges against Anastasio?

   a. The charges were dropped.
   b. He went to jail for a year.
   c. He went to jail for two years.
   d. He received five years' probation.

3. How old was Gordon when he had his first child?

   a. 36
   b. 39
   c. 44

d. 52

4. Gordon likes to share pictures on Facebook of which of the following?

   a. His food
   b. His family
   c. Himself sitting on couches
   d. His DIY escapades

5. True or False: Phish endorsed Senator and Presidential candidate Bernie Sanders. In return, Sanders endorsed the band.

6. What is the name of Jon Fishman's favorite deathgrind band?

   a. Cattle Decapitation
   b. Cephalic Carnage
   c. Terrorizer
   d. Brutal Truth

7. True or False: McConnell's sister has said that she hates Phish's music.

8. How much money did McConnell get from recruiting Anastasio and Fishman to Goddard College in Vermont?

   a. Nothing
   b. $50
   c. $100
   d. $500

9. Anastasio wrote the song "Miss You" about which

of the following people?

   a.   An ex-girlfriend
   b.   A childhood friend
   c.   Jon Fishman
   d.   His sister

10. True or False: When Anastasio's daughter Bella was little, the band set up bounce houses so she could jump during shows.

11. Nowadays, when Anastasio is not on tour, when does he go to sleep?

   a.   8 p.m.
   b.   9 p.m.
   c.   11 p.m.
   d.   1 a.m.

12. True or False: Fishman likes to get naked on stage.

13. Fishman took out a restraining order against which individual in his employment?

   a.   His gardener
   b.   His groundskeeper
   c.   His chimney sweep
   d.   His plumber

14. Which area lifetime achievement award did Fishman win in 2019?

   a.   Syracuse, New York
   b.   Burlington, Vermont
   c.   Philadelphia, Pennsylvania

d. Bangor, Maine

15. Which song inspired Fishman to take drumming lessons?

    a. "Visions of the Emerald Beyond" – Mahavishnu Orchestra

    b. "Summertime Blues" – The Who

    c. "When the Levee Breaks" – Led Zeppelin

    d. "Toad" – Cream

16. Where was Anastasio working when he met his wife, Sue?

    a. A record store

    b. He was already playing with Phish.

    c. A pet store

    d. A gas station

17. Anastasio's mother edited which magazine when he was a kid?

    a. *The Sesame Street Magazine*

    b. *Zoobooks*

    c. *Ranger Rick Jr.*

    d. *Animal Tales*

18. For whom is Phish's music publishing company, Who Is She? Music, named?

    a. Anastasio's daughter

    b. Anastasio's sister

    c. Anastasio's dog

    d. Anastasio's wife

19. True or False: While in college, Anastasio hosted a

morning radio show called *Ambient Alarm Clock*.

20. Anastasio is a football fan. Which team does he support?

    a. The New England Patriots
    b. Dallas Cowboys
    c. New York Jets
    d. Chicago Bears

ANSWERS

1. Trick question – Trey had all of them in his possession. He was charged for "third-degree aggravated unlicensed operation, seventh-degree criminal possession of a controlled substance and DWI – drugs." A police officer saw him crossing into an opposing lane. The singer reportedly told the Chief of Police, "You know what, I've got a problem, and I've got to take care of it. Everything happens for a reason."

2. B – He received five years of probation. Anastasio was sent to drug court instead of a regular one. Luckily for him, he ended up in the Washington County Felony Drug Court, which aims to help individuals overcome drug problems rather than send them to prison. Anastasio has been very vocal in crediting the program for ending his addiction. He said, "The night I got arrested, I couldn't go 10 minutes without taking something." Anastasio testified in Congress in favor of the Drug Court system.

3. C – 44 years old. "I waited until I was older to have a child," Gordon said. "And I was so ready for it. I spend time with her every day, and I don't tour as much as I used to. It's cliché, but I get to see the world through young eyes. It's a unique and

whimsical perspective." Gordon loves touring with his wife and daughter and is very happy that the clean living Phish practices nowadays allows him to do it.

4. C – Himself sitting on couches. He calls this his "Couch Tour." It involves pictures of Gordon sitting on various couches with funny looks on his face.

5. True – Sanders was the mayor of Burlington from 1981 to 1989 during the years when Phish was getting their start. Fishman endorsed Bernie in the Democratic Presidential primaries in 2016 and 2020. The drummer said it was his dedication to upholding Burlington's arts that led him to do so. Before the 2000 elections, Fishman was asked if he supported Bush or Gore, and he answered "Sanders." Meanwhile, Bernie also indicated an appreciation for our legendary jam band. He said they are "one of the greatest bands in the country."

6. A – Cattle Decapitation. Fishman provided narration for one of their albums. Cattle Decapitation vocalist Travis Ryan explains, "Jon is a big fan of the band, and we were happy to have him come on board with the narration, as well as a quote off the top of his head that was inspired by the beautiful area he lives in, and recorded under the Maine night sky."

7. False – His sister Katie helped create the first band

newsletters.

8. C – $100. Goddard College was on the verge of closing. They offered a $50 reward for every student recruited. Anastasio and Fishman joining were part of a successful effort to save the school.

9. B – His sister. Kirsty passed away in 2009.

10. False – But now they have them for the kids that travel with the band!

11. A – 8 p.m. His daughter Bella says, "He is very healthy, meditates, and would go home after The Bakers Dozen [thirteen-night residency at Madison Square Garden] and eat kale chips to unwind. When he's not on tour, he's in bed by, like, 8 p.m. and up at 5 a.m."

12. True – Fishman says he has run around naked a lot since he was a child. He has run naked on stage maybe nine times. Fishman says it's "an impulse control problem." An acquaintance reportedly asked him, "Do you have any f****** idea how illegal that is?" He answered, "Um, well yeah, or not really. I mean, they haven't put me in jail yet."

13. C – His chimney sweep. The chimney sweep had been spreading rumors throughout the community about Fishman. According to the terms of the order, the individual was forbidden from engaging with "intent to harass, torment or threaten" the drummer.

14. A – Syracuse, New York. It is an honor he shares

with Ronnie James Dio and Dick Clark. The drummer modestly said, "Everybody else in that room deserves a lifetime achievement award for what they've done... Do I deserve a lifetime achievement award for being the luckiest kid in the world?"

15. A – "Visions of the Emerald Beyond" – Mahavishnu Orchestra. He had wanted to play before after being inspired by Led Zeppelin and Frank Zappa, but the jazz-fusion outfit made him want to take playing more seriously.

16. C – A pet store.

17. A – *The Sesame Street Magazine*. Dina Anastasio wrote countless children's books over the years. They include *Where is Hollywood?*, *What is the Superbowl?*, *The Hungry Plant* and *Twenty Mini-Mysteries*.

18. C – Anastasio's dog. It was named after Marley, an adorable mixed breed dog who would often tour with the band. She passed away just a few days after Phish went off on their hiatus. She meant a lot to Anastasio. At the end of all of his guitars is Marley's inlaid image saying in a bubble, "I am the Mar Mar." She can also be seen in the "Down with Disease" video.

19. True – Therefore, he felt at home when he revived his radio hosting career on SiriusXM's Phish

Channel. His show is called *Rubber Jungle Radio*.

20. C – New York Jets. McConnell is also a fan. They can often be seen at Jets home games.

DID YOU KNOW?

- Anastasio says that he ended up in a drug tailspin and got arrested because he had difficulty handling the Phish hiatus, which started in 2004. He told GQ, "When I got arrested, I was very sick, and I was in the process of losing everything that was dear to me. I had not played a show for two years and was out of communication with the Phish guys. I was very sick and skinny and crazy and mean. It hurts my head to talk about this stuff, but it's true."

- Many Phish fans like to enjoy the concerts with a bit of help from certain substances. This has not caused any particular problems since Phish fans are usually a very peaceful bunch. However, the NYPD decided to use a series of the band's performances at Madison Square Garden to make mass arrests. To make it worse, they did so on New Year's Eve and the nights leading up to it. Two hundred and thirty-eight arrests were made over those nights. Most of those arrested were for possession of marijuana or ecstasy. While most of those arrested were using for their enjoyment, there were a few serious dealers arrested. One individual had twenty-four capsules of MDMA, seventy-one strips of LSD, and fourteen bags of mushrooms in his possession.

- Anastasio has been sober since 2007 and has not relapsed. He says, however, that he is on guard. "I'm active enough in sobriety that I hear these stories every day. You know, I look to my heroes to be reminded that good, really smart, really talented people can fall into this trap pretty easily, far down the road if they're not careful."

- Jon Fishman and his ex-wife lived on a sustainable farm in Lincolnville, Maine. Fishman's spouse, Briar, has quite a local profile. She opened a General Store for the town, located on 269 Main Street. She has also become an activist fighting against lead paint and pipes in the area. When they moved into their two-hundred-year-old farmhouse, Briar asked the contractor to test for the presence of lead and was told it was all fine. However, when taking her toddler to the pediatrician, they discovered alarming lead levels in his blood. She remembers, "We were terrified. But the doctor said you have lead paint in your environment. Figure it out." The Fishmans found that the culprit was an old fireplace they had removed. They have since donated and worked to raise awareness for the problem. "The education needs to begin when you give birth to your baby. This is something you need to take seriously. This is a major risk," Briar said. "By the time there are symptoms, it's way too late."

- In 2021, Anastasio announced that he was

founding a nonprofit substance use disorder treatment center in Ludlow, Vermont. As a recovering addict, he understands the need for help in the community. He said he talked to several experts on the region and found that "one common thing is there don't seem to be enough beds" for substance use treatment in Vermont. Anastasio told the *Burlington Free Press* in a recent phone conversation, "That seemed like a way to provide and give help. It's not a partisan issue, it's a family issue, and it's an issue of unity."

CHAPTER 9:

JUST GREAT MUSIC

TRIVIA TIME!

1. True or False: During the 2013 Halloween show, the band broke tradition by not playing an entire album.

2. In 2015, the @YEM blog asked fans on Twitter what they thought was the greatest Phish jam of all time. Which performance did the fans choose?
   a. Tweezer – Lake Tahoe, 2013
   b. Providence Bowie – Providence Civic Center, 1994
   c. Went Gin – Limestone, ME, 1997
   d. Albany YEM – Albany, NY, 1995

3. How many shows has Phish played in their career (as of early 2021)?
   a. 1129
   b. 1529
   c. 1829
   d. 2229

4. True or False: Although they do not usually do teasers of songs before they've been released, Phish played a bit of "Mozambique" on the Island Tour of 1998.

5. In which year was the album *Junta* first released on vinyl?

    a. 1989
    b. 1992
    c. 2001
    d. 2012

6. Which Phish album was produced by legendary producer Bob Ezrin?

    a. *Joy*
    b. *Fuego*
    c. *Big Boat*
    d. *Sigma Oasis*

7. On the *Hampton Comes Alive* album, the band covers which unlikely 90s hit?

    a. "Boombastic" – Shaggy
    b. "Barbie Girl" – Aqua
    c. "MMMBop" – Hanson
    d. "Gettin' Jiggy Wit It" – Will Smith

8. What was the name of Anastasio's band when he attended the Taft School?

    a. Space Antelope
    b. Dogs Die in Hot Cars

c. Crispy Ambulance

d. Totally Enormous Extinct Dinosaurs

9. "You Enjoy Myself" is probably the most famous Phish song of all. In which year did they debut it in concert?

   a. 1985
   b. 1986
   c. 1987
   d. 1988

10. True or False: The song "Faht" off the album *Pictures of Nectar* is the only song on that album to have never been played live.

11. Which is the best-selling Phish studio album?

   a. *Hoist*
   b. *Pictures of Nectar*
   c. *Stash*
   d. *Rift*

12. The last time the band played a complete set of songs from the fictional Gamehendge world with narration was in which year?

   a. 1992
   b. 1994
   c. 1999
   d. 2017

13. Anastasio was inspired by several fantasy writers to create the Gamehendge world. The band even

wrote a song about characters from one of their favorite fantasy writers. Which writer enjoyed this honor?

    a. J.R.R. Tolkien

    b. C.S. Lewis

    c. George Lucas

    d. Terry Pratchett

14. The band selected most of the songs for *A Live One* through a meticulous internal process. However, they let the fans pick their favorites through the rec.music.phish Usenet Newsgroup as well. Which track on the album was included thanks to the fans' votes?

    a. "Simple"

    b. "Stash"

    c. "Harry Hood"

    d. "Gumbo"

15. In 1997, a compilation album called *Stash* was released in which region(s)?

    a. Only in Japan

    b. Only in North America

    c. Only in Europe

    d. Only in Canada and Australia

16. The cover of *Billy Breathes* is an extreme and unflattering closeup of which band member?

    a. Trey Anastasio

    b. Tom Marshall

    c. Jon Fishman

d. Mike Gordon

17. Most of the songs on *Story of the Ghost* were written through jams and then developed into songs in the studio. Which song on the album had been previously performed?

    a. "Guyute"
    b. "Limb by Limb"
    c. "The Momma Dance"
    d. "Frankie Says"

18. The massive live album *Hampton Comes Alive* has forty-eight tracks in total. How many of them are cover versions?

    a. 5
    b. 10
    c. 15
    d. 20

19. Phish doesn't usually play its music on the tour bus. But there is one album that was on regular rotation for a while. Which album was it?

    a. *Siket Disc*
    b. *Junta*
    c. *Billy Breathes*
    d. *Farmhouse*

20. How long did it take the band to record the album *Round Room*?

    a. One day

b. Four days
c. A week
d. Ten days

ANSWERS

1. False – Or, sort of false. Instead of covering an entire album by another band, they played their whole (at that time) upcoming album *Wingsuit*.

2. A – Tweezer – Lake Tahoe, 2013. It is an absolute masterpiece without a single wasted note despite going on for no less than 36 minutes. By the way, the answers are in the order of votes received.

3. C – 1829.

4. True – They played a bit of the song during one of their shows in 1998. However, they first played the whole "Mozambique" number on September 9, 1999.

5. D – 2012. It came out as a limited edition three-record set. Only 5,000 copies were released.

6. C – *Big Boat*. Ezrin tried to get the band to dig deeper into their emotions than they ever had before. However, the fan base has been quite critical of the result.

7. D – "Getting' Jiggy Wit It" – Will Smith. It was the first rap song the band played in its entirety.

8. A – Space Antelope. The band included his friend Steve "the Dude of Life" Pollack. There is a pretty

cool clip of them playing the Grateful Dead song "Franklin's Tower" in 1982 available online.

9. B – 1986. Although, if you said 1985, you might be correct. Some argue that the song was first played earlier. The show took place in Burlington on February 3, 1986. It was a benefit for the African National Congress, which at that time was fighting against apartheid. Alongside the band, it also featured South African dub poet Zenzilé Madikinea.

10. False – It has been played twelve times, the least of any song on the album. However, the last time was in 1995.

11. A – *Hoist*. The album was certified gold by the RIAA on August 19, 1996. It also reached the top 40 of the Mainstream Rock Tracks chart. At least to an extent, the album broke into the mainstream on the strength of the "Down with Disease" single.

12. B – 1994. The show was at the Great Woods Center for the Performing Arts in Mansfield, MA.

13. C – C.S. Lewis. The song is "Prince Caspian." The band's fan base is split on the song. Some see it as a classic, while others take it as an opportunity to go on a bathroom break. Nonetheless, it is one of Anastasio's favorites and is played regularly at shows.

14. B – "Stash." The fans selected the July 8, 1994

version of the song. It's a highlight of that classic album.

15. C – Only in Europe. It was released to promote the band on the continent before their 1996 spring tour of Europe, opening for Santana.

16. D – Mike Gordon. It was the first time a member of the band appeared on the cover of an album. Anastasio remembers, "We finished *Billy Breathes*, and our manager kept saying, 'What are you going to do about the cover?' So, finally, it was the LAST day, and it was, like three in the morning. They (management) said, 'We NEED a cover tomorrow.' You know all those pictures on the back? We cut them out and stuck them on with scotch tape. Mike was on the cover. He just shot a picture of himself. The whole thing took like five minutes!" However, some members of the band and those close to them have come to regret their choice of album cover. Both Anastasio and Tom Marshall have said that it ruins the enjoyment of the album for them.

17. A – "Guyute"

18. 18 D – 20. The covers run the gamut of styles, some being serious tributes and others whimsical tongue-in-cheek nods. The artists covered include Jimi Hendrix, Stevie Wonder, the Beastie Boys, Will Smith, and The Beatles. We will let you figure out which is which.

19. A – *Siket Disc*. Gordon recalls that when touring in

the early 2000s, "It fit the vibe perfectly... It's one of the only instances I can remember when we regularly played our own music."

20. B – Four days. The band was raring to go after a two-year hiatus. They met up at the Barn studio and bashed the album out. *Rolling Stone* magazine noted "a decidedly live" feeling and it "breathes with an anxious, edge-of-the-seat intensity that's missing from their previous studio efforts."

DID YOU KNOW?

- Although certainly not a mainstream act, Phish has not been ignored by the Recording Academy. In 2000, they were nominated for Best Rock Instrumental Performance for the song "First Tube." They were also nominated that same year for Best Boxed Set Packaging for *Hampton Comes Alive*. Phish fans were not impressed because many believe that award shows are phony. They were even less impressed when Phish lost!

- Jon Fishman appeared in the cult movie *My X-Girlfriend's Wedding Reception* as a transexual drummer named Ginger. Wikipedia describes the plot as, "A woman's ex-boyfriend becomes the member of a band at an Italian Jewish wedding." The movie was filmed in Burlington, Vermont. It is also notable for featuring Bernie Sanders as Rabbi Manny Schewitz.

- Phish took interaction with their fans during shows to a whole other level by playing chess with them. They had repeated games against their fans starting in 1995. The games proceeded at a slow match, with about two moves per show. The band won the first game and taunted the audience with a rendition of "We Are the Champions." In 2020, they tried to put together a rematch through

Chess.com, but the website servers collapsed as a result. In the end, the band won again.

- In the early days of the band's formation and growing fanbase, Phish only played concerts and live performances in the New England area, mainly Vermont. In 1988, the band decided to embark on a small tour in the west. They traveled to Colorado, where they enjoyed playing seven different gigs over ten days. This small tour was recorded and released as a live album titled *Colorado '88* in 2006. In his book, Gordon explains how that tour came about: "My fiance Cilla Foster was responsible for our first tour. In 1988 she was waitressing in Telluride for a guy named Warren Stickney. I didn't know her very well at the time, but one day she called and said Stickney wanted us to come play in his bar. We'd never played further away from home than New Hampshire at the time, but Stickney promised to book a monthlong tour across the country. It took another six months to get him on the phone again, but I finally spoke with him about a week before we were supposed to hit the road. He said something like, 'I don't know if I can get you any other gigs, but you can play my place and I'll pay you a thousand bucks.' I couldn't get him on the phone after that, so the six of us - including Paul Languedoc and Tim Rogers, who was doing lights - decided to go for it anyway.

- "We finished playing a Nectar's gig at 2am, took a vote, and decided to head west then and there. Our friends Ninja Custodian subbed for us the next night at Nectar's, and we took off across the country with turkey ham, cheese, and apple butter. It was the middle of summer, and we were traveling in a windowless truck with only a foam mattress on the floor. We didn't even stop at a rest area for forty hours, so the truck got pretty disgusting."

CONCLUSION

After recounting the beginning, the middle, and the end of the fantastical career Phish has created for themselves, it is undeniable how influential and unique the band really is. Renowned for their wild live performances and bending the rules of rock, Phish's live shows are nothing short of legendary. Their projected aesthetic of going against the grain has appealed to their fanatical fan base.

With the band still active today, the eccentric and bizarre sounds that Phish trailblazed continues to live on!

We hope you enjoyed this book and please leave a review where you bought it.